Kay and Martez

Unit 7 Reader

Skills Strand

GRADE 1

Amplify learning.

Table of Contents

Kay and Martez

Unit 7 Reader

Martez, Martez, Martez

K**ay**'s dad checks K**ay**'s plate.

"K**ay**," he says, "have some of your coleslaw! Food is not free!"

K**ay** smiles. "Food is not free" is something her dad says a lot. He is a man who likes to save as much cash as he can. He hates p**ay**ing for food that ends up in the trash.

K**ay** cuts her pork chop and lifts a bite of it into the **ai**r.

"Martez likes pork chops," K**ay** says. "But he hates coleslaw."

K**ay** pops the bite of pork chop in her mouth. Then she says, "Martez likes to pl**ay** hopscotch and draw pictures with cr**ay**ons."

After a bit, she adds, "Martez can run the fastest on the pl**ay**ground."

"Martez, Martez, Martez!" says K**ay**'s dad. "Who is this Martez?"

"He's my pal."

"Is Martez in your class?" asks K**ay**'s mom.

K**ay** nods.

"Is he nice?"

"He is the best!"

"So should we invite Martez to visit us for dinner?"

"Yes!" says K**ay** with a shout. "Can we invite him tomorrow?"

Dinner with Kay

The next d**ay**, Martez visits K**ay**'s house for dinner. K**ay**'s mom serves corn on the cob.

Martez tells K**ay**'s mom, "I like this corn a lot! You are a good cook!"

"Thank you!" says K**ay**'s mom.

"I got the corn on sale!" K**ay**'s dad brags. K**ay**'s dad smiles. He is proud to think that he got good corn for such a good price.

Martez says, "This corn is so sweet. You are a good shopper."

After dinner, K**ay** and Martez run outside. They splash in the pool and pl**ay** tag.

While doing the dishes, K**ay**'s mom says, "What good manners that Martez has!"

"Yes," says K**ay**'s dad. "And he ate all of the food on his plate!"

When pl**ay**time is finished, Martez runs inside to thank K**ay**'s mom and dad for dinner.

Then he asks, "Can K**ay** have dinner at our house tomorrow?"

K**ay**'s mom and dad s**ay** she can. They like Martez.

The Red Dish

The next d**ay**, K**ay** has dinner with Martez and his mom and dad. Martez's mom and dad are from Mexico.

They have a Mexican dish with peppers, corn, and rice all mixed up. There are two dishes of it sitting side by side. One dish is red. One is green.

"Are the two dishes the same?" K**ay** asks.

"Nope," says Martez with a smile. "The stuff in the red dish has lots of hot peppers. The stuff in the green dish has just green peppers, which are not as hot."

Martez points at his dad and says, "My dad likes hot peppers."

His dad smiles and nods.

Martez asks K**ay**, "Do you like hot peppers?"

K**ay** shrugs. She has never had hot peppers.

K**ay** has some food from the green dish. She likes it a lot. She says, "Could I have some from the red dish?"

"You can, but it's hot, hot, hot!" says Martez. "We have a s**ay**ing in our house: *He is a brave man who has food from dad's red dish!*"

"Brave or perhaps foolish!" says his mom.

K**ay** is brave—or perhaps foolish. She takes a bite of the peppers from the red dish. Martez looks at her. His mom and dad look, too.

"Do you like it?" asks Martez.

K**ay**'s face starts to get red. She yells, "Hot!"

Her face gets redder and redder.

Martez sees that K**ay** is in p**ai**n. He brings her ice cubes. K**ay** stuffs some in her mouth and lets them melt. The ice cubes help cool down her mouth.

"Ug!" K**ay** says, sitting back from her plate. "Those peppers in the red dish are too hot for me! I need to stick to the green dish."

"Still," Martez says, "tod**ay** you joined the club."

"What club?"

"The I-ate-from-dad's-red-dish-and-am-still-living-to-tell-the-tale club!" says Martez.

Martez and his mom and dad all smile. They like Kay.

In the Mail

In the summer, Martez takes a trip to Mexico with his Mom and Dad. He sends K**ay** a card with a picture of a place in Mexico on it.

The card says, "K**ay**, I am on a trip with my mom and dad. It is fun, but I miss you. I can't w**ai**t to get back so we can pl**ay**." Then there are some words that K**ay** can't make out.

"Mom!" K**ay** says, "Martez wrote me this card, but I think the last part of it is written in Mexican."

K**ay**'s mom looks at the card. She smiles. "That's not Mexican," she says. "It's Spanish. Lots of Mexicans write in Spanish."

MEXICO
Kay,
I am on a trip with
my mom and dad. It is
fun, but I miss you.
I can't wait to get back
so we can play.
¡Eres mi mejor amigo!
¡Hasta pronto!

"Why do they write in Spanish?" K**ay** asks.

"Well, you see, w**ay** back in the past, men from Sp**ai**n came to Mexico. Because the men from Sp**ai**n spoke and wrote Spanish, the Mexicans began to talk and write in Spanish, too. And that is why, to this d**ay**, lots of Mexicans still talk and write in Spanish."

"But what do the words s**ay**?"

"Let me see," says K**ay**'s mom. "I took a Spanish class. Martez says, 'You are my best pal. See you soon!'"

K**ay** hugs the card and shouts, "Martez is the best!"

MEXICO

The Holiday

When Martez gets back from his trip, he invites K**ay** to visit him at home.

When K**ay** steps in, she sees lots of singing and dancing. There is a flag with green, white, and red stripes pinned up in the living room.

"What's up?" K**ay** asks.

Martez expl**ai**ns, "Tod**ay** is September 16th. It is a big holid**ay** for Mexicans."

"On this d**ay**," Martez expl**ai**ns, "we p**ay** tribute to a man who helped set Mexico free from the Spanish. You see, for a long time, the Spanish were in charge in Mexico. All of the land in Mexico was theirs. They could tell Mexicans what to do. They made the Mexicans do all of the hard jobs. Then one man got tired of it and set out to make things better."

Martez points at a picture and says, "This is the man who started it all. His name was Hidalgo. He made a speech. He said the Mexicans should be free from the Spanish."

"Did they do it?" asks K**ay**.

"Yes. It took a long time, but in the end, they did."

"Is it sort of like when the U.S. broke free from the British?" K**ay** asks.

"Yes, yes!" Martez says. "It is just like that!"

K**ay** points at the flag. It has three stripes: one green, one white, and one red. "Is that the Mexican flag?" she asks.

"Yes," says Martez. "That is our flag."

Then Martez stretches out his hand and says, "Would you dance a Mexican dance with me?"

Better Than the Best

K**ay** has started to spend a lot of time with Martez.

She has started to use some Spanish words, too.

When her dad spoons rice onto her plate one d**ay**, K**ay** says *gracias*. Then she expl**ai**ns that *gracias* is Spanish for *thank you*.

K**ay**'s mom says, "K**ay**, would you like to have a chance to use those Spanish words of yours in Mexico?"

"Are you kidding?" K**ay** excl**ai**ms. "That would be the best!"

"Well, your dad and I have planned a trip to Mexico."

K**ay** shouts, "Yippee!"

K**ay**'s mom has a big smile on her face. She says, "How would you like to bring Martez with you on the trip?"

K**ay**'s jaw drops. "If Martez is on the trip, that would be better than the best!" she says.

Her mom adds, "Martez just needs to ask his mom and dad."

K**ay** jumps up and shouts, "I can't w**ai**t to tell Martez!"

The Long Cab Ride

K**ay** and Martez just got to Mexico with K**ay**'s mom and dad. They are at the **ai**rport. They are looking for a cab that will take them to the place where they are st**ay**ing.

K**ay**'s dad waves his hand and gets a cab.

8928

A man jumps out of a cab and shouts, "Greetings! I'm Carlos. Where can I drive you on this fine d**ay**?"

"To the inn," says K**ay**'s dad.

Carlos steps on the gas. The cab picks up speed.

"I will take you to the inn," Carlos says, "and on the w**ay** I will take you to see some nice sites here in Mexico. There are lots of nice sites on the w**ay**, or just out of the w**ay** a bit."

"Thanks," says K**ay**'s dad, "but we are tired from the trip. So you can just take us to where we are st**ay**ing."

"Here in Mexico," Carlos says, "we have all sorts of land. There are hills and pl**ai**ns. There are deserts, r**ai**nforests, and wetlands. I will take you to see some wetlands on the w**ay**! They are not far out of the w**ay**."

"Wetlands?" says K**ay**'s dad. "Where's the inn?" He starts to s**ay** something else, but K**ay**'s mom jabs him in the back.

"Hush!" she whispers. "Let him share."

TAXI

Carlos waves his hands and describes things as he drives.

Should you use those hands to drive the cab?" K**ay**'s dad asks.

But Carlos keeps talking. "On the left, you can see a soccer game. Soccer is a big sport in Mexico."

"That is an Aztec shrine," Carlos says.

"Here is a good place for shopping."

"That is my mom's house."

At last, the cab zips up to the inn.

Carlos tells K**ay**'s dad the price of the cab ride. K**ay**'s dad is upset. It was a long ride, and he must p**ay** a lot. He hates to p**ay** so much. But what can he do?

The Vote

The next morning, K**ay**'s dad is still upset that the cab ride cost s**o** much. But K**ay**'s mom is not.

"You m**ay** think I'm nuts," she says, "but I liked that cab ride yesterd**ay**. I liked having someone in the car who could tell us what's what."

K**ay** says, "I liked that, too."

K**ay**'s dad looks at Martez and says, "Did you like it, too?"

TAXI

Martez shrugs and says, "Well … I sort of … did … like it."

K**ay**'s mom says, "I think we should hire someone who has a car and can tell us what there is to see down here in Mexico. The man at the desk gave me a name. He says this man—Mister Gomez is his name—has a car. If we hire him, he will drive us to see all of the best sites."

"But that will cost a lot!" says K**ay**'s dad. "Why should we p**ay** when we can see all the same sites by ourselves? Look, I got this book on Mexico in a used bookshop. It will tell us all of the same stuff that the man would tell us! And it has lots of pictures!"

MEXICO
ON 30 BUCKS
A DAY

"It's not the same!" says K**ay**'s mom. "And that book of yours is out of date. Let's have a vote. Who votes we hire Mister Gomez?"

K**ay**'s mom r**ai**ses her hand at once. K**ay**'s hand shoots up fast, too. Martez w**ai**ts a bit. Then he r**ai**ses his hand as well.

"That's three votes for Mister Gomez and one vote for your book," b**oa**sts K**ay**'s mom.

K**ay**'s dad gr**oa**ns.

Mister Gomez

Mister Gomez is at the inn the next morning. He takes them outside and points to a stone with his cane.

"This stone has stood here for a long, long time," Mister Gomez says. "It has stood here much longer than me. This stone is from the time of the Aztec Empire."

"The what?" K**ay** asks.

"The Aztec Empire," says Mister Gomez. "Back in the past, Aztec men cut stones like this one and stacked them up to make shrines to their gods."

"The Aztecs had lots of gods," Mister Gomez says. "They had a sun god, a moon god, and a r**ai**n god. Then, one d**ay**, the Spanish came. They were led by a man named Cortez. His g**oa**l was to be in charge of Mexico."

"Cortez led his men on a long march. He and his men kept marching until they got to the spot where we are standing. Here they clashed with the Aztec troops. The Aztec troops were brave, but in the end, the Spanish came out on top. Cortez and his men were in charge of Mexico."

"Cortez and the Spanish did not respect the Aztecs. The Spanish knocked down the Aztec shrines and used the stones to make r**oa**ds and streets and forts."

Mister Gomez waves his cane and says, "Lots of the stones in this square were cut back in Aztec times. They were used to make Aztec shrines. Then they were used by Cortez and the Spanish. And we still use them today."

Martez says, "That is so cool that we are standing on the same stones!"

The smile on K**ay**'s face tells that she thinks so, too.

K**ay**'s mom jabs K**ay**'s dad in the side and says, "Looks like we are fine without that book of yours!"

A House in the Clouds

The next d**ay**, Mister Gomez takes Martez, K**ay**, and K**ay**'s mom and dad on a trip.

In the car, Mister Gomez says, "You will like this next place. The stones there have stood for much, much longer than the last stones."

When they get to the site, they see three vast piles of stone, all of which rise to a point and seem to scrape the clouds. One of them is so big that Kay and Martez have to tilt their necks all the w**ay** back to see the top of it.

"Goodness!" says K**ay**'s mom.

"Cool!" says Martez.

"Was this a shrine?" K**ay**'s mom asks.

"Yes," says Mister Gomez. "This was a shrine to a snake god. That one there was a shrine to the sun god. And that one was a shrine to the moon god."

"Were they Aztec shrines?" Martez asks.

"Sort of," Mister Gomez says. "The Aztecs came after. The shrines were set up w**ay** back in the past. But the Aztecs came here and added to the shrines. This was an important place for them. They came here to offer gifts to their gods."

"Can we get to the top of one of them?" asks K**ay**.

"Yes, you can," says Mister Gomez, "if your mom and dad s**ay** it's fine. But you must grab on to the rope."

K**ay** and Martez make their w**ay** to the top.

It takes them a long time to get there. From the top, they can see for miles and miles.

Martez yells, "K**ay** and I have a house in the clouds!"

K**ay** says, "Look! Mom and Dad look like bugs from up here!"

K**ay** waves her hands at her mom and dad. They wave back.

The Market

The next d**ay**, K**ay** and her mom take a trip to a street market. Mister Gomez joins them.

At the market, all sorts of things are on sale. Some men are selling food. Some are selling arts and crafts. There are p**ai**ntings and knickknacks and cloth stitched in fun patterns.

10
MEXICO

One man is selling masks.

K**ay**'s mom spots a mask that she likes. It is a red mask with glitter. She looks at the price tag and gr**oa**ns.

"I can't p**ay** that much," she tells K**ay**. "We need to stick to our spending limit."

"See if you can get it for less," says Mister Gomez. "I'll bet he will dicker with you on the price."

K**ay**'s mom asks the man, "Will you take ten for this?"

"No! " the man says. "I p**ai**nted it by hand! Fifteen!"

"That is too much for me," K**ay**'s mom says. "I will p**ay** you twelve."

The man says, "Fifteen! N**o** less."

K**ay**'s mom sets down the mask and starts to look at the next booth.

"No, no!" the man yells. "Stay! I will sell it to you for twelve!"

He hands her the mask. She grins and p**ay**s the man.

"W**ay** to go, Mom!" says K**ay**, "I am impressed."

"So am I!" says Mister Gomez with a smile.

A Rainforest Ride

The next d**ay**, they s**ay** farewell to Mister Gomez. K**ay**'s dad rents a car to take them to see the r**ai**nforest.

In the r**ai**nforest, it is hot and wet. A thick l**ay**er of trees blocks out part of the sun.

K**ay**'s mom drives. K**ay**'s dad shares facts from his book.

As they drive, K**ay** spots a zip line that children can ride.

MEXICO

"Mom, Dad!" she yells. "Can we stop and ride the zip line? It looks like so much fun!"

K**ay**'s mom parks the car. The zip line runs from a tree house down to the ground.

"Is it safe?" K**ay**'s mom asks the man in charge.

"Yes," says the man. "It's safe. The children ride in a harness. And there is a net down there to catch them, just in case."

Kay's mom thinks it looks safe. She pays the man and gets two tickets, one for Kay and one for Martez.

Martez gets belted into the harness. Then he rides the zip line. He shouts as he slides down the line.

Kay yells down, "Is it fun, Martez?"

Martez yells back, "It's the best!"

Kay gets belted in. She has a fun ride, too.

The Dive

K**ay**'s dad drives to the c**oa**st of the Gulf of Mexico. For two d**ay**s, the children s**oa**k up the sun and swim in the pool.

On d**ay** three, they dive in the Gulf of Mexico. They rent masks, fins, and tanks of **ai**r. Then a man brings them out to the dive site in a b**oa**t. The dive site is a reef where a Spanish ship sank.

They jump in and swim down. With their fins on, they can swim fast. With their masks on, they can see a long way down. They see fish and crabs. Martez spots a starfish.

Martez and K**ay** look for the Spanish ship. They swim down until they see it. They see fish swimming in and out of it. Then they swim back up.

At the Airport

The trip has ended. It is time to get back to the U.S.

K**ay**'s dad drives to the **ai**rport. K**ay**'s mom st**ay**s with K**ay** and Martez while he drops off the car.

K**ay** and Martez pl**ay** with an **ai**rplane and toss it in the **ai**r. It makes a big loop and glides down.

K**ay**'s dad had fun on the trip, but he spent a lot of cash. He takes what is left of his Mexican cash and has it turned back into U.S. cash.

At the ticket counter, K**ay**'s dad takes charge. He barks out orders.

"This w**ay,** K**ay**!"

"St**ay** close to me, Martez!"

"Children, get out your passports!"

The children get their passports out. K**ay**'s mom gets hers out. But K**ay**'s dad's is nowhere to be found.

$PES

He unzips his bag to look for it. Soon he is digging in the bag, tossing things this w**ay** and that. At last, he sees his passport.

"Here it is!" he says, with a sheepish look.

Martez, K**ay,** and her mom all smile. K**ay**'s dad sometimes has a hard time keeping track of things.

"Dad," K**ay** says, "maybe you should sit back and let Mom take charge for a while."

About this Book

This book has been created for use by students learning to read with the Core Knowledge Reading Program. Readability levels are suitable for early readers. The book has also been carefully leveled in terms of its "code load," or the number of spellings used in the stories.

The English writing system is complex. It uses more than 200 spellings to stand for 40-odd sounds. Many sounds can be spelled several different ways, and many spellings can be pronounced several different ways. This book has been designed to make early reading experiences simpler and more productive by using a subset of the available spellings. It uses *only* spellings that students have been taught to sound out as part of their phonics lessons, plus a handful of Tricky Words, which have also been deliberately introduced in the lessons. This means that the stories will be 100% decodable if they are assigned at the proper time.

As the students move through the program, they learn new spellings and the "code load" in the decodable Readers increases gradually. The code load graphic on this page indicates the number of spellings students are expected to know in order to read the first story of the book and the number of spellings students are expected to know in order to read the final stories in the book. The columns on the inside back cover list the specific spellings and Tricky Words students are expected to recognize at the beginning of this Reader. The bullets at the bottom of the inside back cover identify spellings, Tricky Words, and other topics that are introduced gradually in the unit this Reader accompanies.

Visit us on the web at www.coreknowledge.org

Core Knowledge Language Arts

Series Editor-in-Chief
E. D. Hirsch, Jr.

President
Linda Bevilacqua

Editorial Staff
Carolyn Gosse, Senior Editor - Preschool
Khara Turnbull, Materials Development Manager
Michelle L. Warner, Senior Editor - Listening & Learning

Mick Anderson
Robin Blackshire
Maggie Buchanan
Paula Coyner
Sue Fulton
Sara Hunt
Erin Kist
Robin Luecke
Rosie McCormick
Cynthia Peng
Liz Pettit
Ellen Sadler
Deborah Samley
Diane Auger Smith
Sarah Zelinke

Design and Graphics Staff
Scott Ritchie, Creative Director

Kim Berrall
Michael Donegan
Liza Greene
Matt Leech
Bridget Moriarty
Lauren Pack

Consulting Project Management Services
ScribeConcepts.com

Additional Consulting Services
Ang Blanchette
Dorrit Green
Carolyn Pinkerton

Acknowledgments

These materials are the result of the work, advice, and encouragement of numerous individuals over many years. Some of those singled out here already know the depth of our gratitude; others may be surprised to find themselves thanked publicly for help they gave quietly and generously for the sake of the enterprise alone. To helpers named and unnamed we are deeply grateful.

Contributors to Earlier Versions of these Materials
Susan B. Albaugh, Kazuko Ashizawa, Nancy Braier, Kathryn M. Cummings, Michelle De Groot, Diana Espinal, Mary E. Forbes, Michael L. Ford, Ted Hirsch, Danielle Knecht, James K. Lee, Diane Henry Leipzig, Martha G. Mack, Liana Mahoney, Isabel McLean, Steve Morrison, Juliane K. Munson, Elizabeth B. Rasmussen, Laura Tortorelli, Rachael L. Shaw, Sivan B. Sherman, Miriam E. Vidaver, Catherine S. Whittington, Jeannette A. Williams

We would like to extend special recognition to Program Directors Matthew Davis and Souzanne Wright who were instrumental to the early development of this program.

Schools
We are truly grateful to the teachers, students, and administrators of the following schools for their willingness to field test these materials and for their invaluable advice: Capitol View Elementary, Challenge Foundation Academy (IN), Community Academy Public Charter School, Lake Lure Classical Academy, Lepanto Elementary School, New Holland Core Knowledge Academy, Paramount School of Excellence, Pioneer Challenge Foundation Academy, New York City PS 26R (The Carteret School), PS 30X (Wilton School), PS 50X (Clara Barton School), PS 96Q, PS 102X (Joseph O. Loretan), PS 104Q (The Bays Water), PS 214K (Michael Friedsam), PS 223Q (Lyndon B. Johnson School), PS 308K (Clara Cardwell), PS 333Q (Goldie Maple Academy), Sequoyah Elementary School, South Shore Charter Public School, Spartanburg Charter School, Steed Elementary School, Thomas Jefferson Classical Academy, Three Oaks Elementary, West Manor Elementary.

And a special thanks to the CKLA Pilot Coordinators Anita Henderson, Yasmin Lugo-Hernandez, and Susan Smith, whose suggestions and day-to-day support to teachers using these materials in their classrooms was critical.

Credits

Writers

Katy Duffield, Anna Kavalauskas, Mary Miller, Susannah Myers,
Juliane Munson, Matthew Davis

Illustrators and Image Sources

All illustrations by Dustin Mackay